Bristle the Red

by Wendy Ellwood

Illustrated by Sophie Holme

Three Little Red Squirrels
Chitter chatter, chitter chatter,
Bristle, Peg and Ping
Nitter natter, nitter natter.

Quick! They're chasing after me!
I bound towards the nearest tree.
They've nearly got me by my tail,
I leap for a higher branch but fail.

I fall to the ground with a bit of a bump,
They land on me in a furry lump.
Then both of them are off at a run.
My turn to chase them, we have such fun!

We dart round High Hay, amongst the trees
Looking for pine cones, berries and seeds.
We call this special place our home,
Here my family is free to roam.

I am called Bristle because my tail's like a brush;
It sweeps all around me in a hairy, red rush.

DOINK!

Ping, my brother, can hear a pin drop
With tufty ears that listen nonstop.

Peg my sister is thoughtful and shy;
She flits around like a butterfly.

There are lots of cousins to be found
Playing in the trees, darting around.

Last but not least comes our special Mar,
(Real name Marmalade), the best mum by far.

Now, I want to tell you what happened to me
When early one day I sneaked down from our tree.

Mar, Ping and Peg still slept in the drey.
I was wide awake, wanting to play.
Mar warned us not to go out alone
But, liking mischief, I went on my own.

I saw something grey at the foot of our tree,
Though just what it was I couldn't quite see.
It looked like a brush, a furry grey lump,
Suddenly it moved and made me jump!

I crept up close, as brave as can be ...

"Hi," he replied, "I'm just nosing around.
Looking for anything good to be found!"

I said it was strange I'd not seen him before.
"I'm a Yankee Grey, on a Lake District tour."

I was relieved to see him go off on his way.
With a sinister smile he said,

Have a nice day.

I darted back to Mar in our warm, safe drey
To tell her I'd encountered a Yankee Grey.

"Bristle, it sounds like you
were having a dream,
Everyone knows squirrels
are red-brown and cream.
But make very sure
you stay together,
No wandering off on
your own, not ever!"

I woke up early the very next morning
And ran down the tree, not heeding Mar's warning.

I was amazed to see grey tails galore,
Led by the Grey I had met once before,
Marching toward me like an army at war.

"Wh- what do you want?" I spoke through my fear.
"We want this here wood," he said with a sneer.
"I'm Kernal Nutcase, don't mess with me,
By early morning, be out of this tree".
I bravely squeaked, "Please leave us alone
And go directly back to your OWN home."

"We are Yankee Greys, we came here by boat,
Had a rough, rocky journey, just stayed afloat.
We've left our land, need a place to call home,
This wood will do, we'll make it our own."

"What you're proposing is quite, quite wrong,
High Hay is the Wood where WE belong"

Then he stomped away with his tail in the air,
Greys marching behind him without a care.

I was frightened, shaking, full of dread.
I raced to tell Mar what had been said.

She told us to inform Wainwright Owl
About the Greys and their plot most foul.

Up the tree we scampered, near up to the sky,
Watching swifts and swallows and buzzards fly by.
We saw Wainwright Owl emerge from a cloud,

Big eyes, flapping wings, Twit-t-wooing out loud.

"Let me look at my map and make a plan,
I'll consult Queen B Potter if I can."

We darted round in a panic together,
While Mar and Owl hatched a plan so clever.
Then Owl flew off, his wings in a flurry,
The sun had set, we were all in a hurry.

Mar summoned us to hear the cunning plan,

"Collect as many conkers and cones as you can.
Bristle, sweep them up in a mighty mound,
Ping, listen out for any warning sound.
Peg, help take them to the drey to store
Then straight back down to search for more."

No time to sleep before day was dawning,
All awaiting this fearful morning.

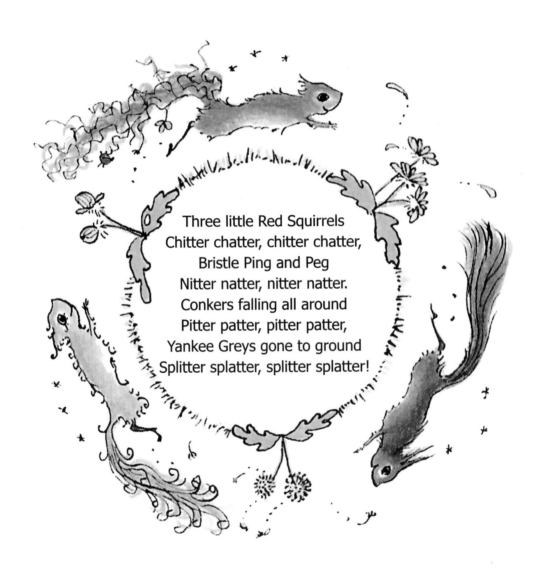

Three little Red Squirrels
Chitter chatter, chitter chatter,
Bristle Ping and Peg
Nitter natter, nitter natter.
Conkers falling all around
Pitter patter, pitter patter,
Yankee Greys gone to ground
Splitter splatter, splitter splatter!

Part 2

Next day as the sun rose in the sky
All our Lakeland friends were standing by.

Queen B Potter granted Lion the right
To come from Helm Crag, with lamb, to fight.

There was lion, Doe deer, rabbits and moles,
Hedgehogs, Herdie, stoats and voles,
Badgers and fox and little birds blue,
Hares and ferrets and red cousins too.

Owl stood in our midst
with Mar by his side.
"Fight bravely, my friends,
but first you must...
HIDE!"

Not a sound could be heard, not a rustle or murmur.
We waited so bravely; we could NOT have stood firmer.

Ping warned us when he heard the distant noise
Of Nutcase on the march with his Yankee boys.

The minutes ticked by, the air laden with fear.
We stood like statues, not a breath could you hear.

Suddenly, a rushing along the ground,
A jumping and a leaping all around.

Leading his gang came Kernal Nutcase.
He stepped up to Wainwright and stared face to face.

"Kernal Nutcase, you think you've caught us.
Wrong! You're surrounded by our supporters.
But I am wise and I will do you a deal.
Think about it carefully, it might appeal."

"We don't want deals, you silly old bird,
Clear off right now, not another word."

As Nutcase gave Wainwright a mighty shove
We actioned our plan from ground and above.

We had collected conkers and cones by the ton.

Now we fired
them all,
like bullets
from a gun.

From behind every tree, out stepped a friend,
Loyal to Reds from beginning to end.

Then as Helm Crag Lion gave a monstrous roar
Scared Yankee greys cowered on the floor.
"Ouch ," they shouted as they were hit on the head.
"Ok!" shouted Nutcase, "Tell us your plan instead."

"I propose to take you on a long, hard trek
Over fells and lakes and babbling becks.
I will leave you when we reach Morecambe Bay,
Across the moving sands you can make your way
To vast forests with trees of every kind
All the food you could want, there you will find.

Make silver dreys, line them with gold
Sleep in them and never grow old.

Only I know of this mysterious land.
Will you follow me to the moving sand?"

Nutcase imagined what Owl had evoked.
He rubbed his nose, pulled a face, then he spoke:
"We will follow you to our promised land.
Give us a hoot when we reach the sand."

Owl led them away; we Reds were relieved,
Not suspecting the Greys had been deceived!

Wainwright Owl flew back, mission completed.
We asked if the Greys had been defeated.
"Did they reach their wood? Did they cross the bay?
If they don't like it, might they return one day?"

Owl listened patiently, cleared his throat,
He looked all around, and then he spoke ...

"The greys followed me as far as the Bay,
Surrounded in mist as they made their way!"

So many questions, things we wanted to know,
"Did they get swallowed up? Was the quick sand slow?
Did it squelch and squash? Did it hubble and bubble?
Did they get half way across and realise the trouble?"

"The main thing", said Owl, "is they won't be back.
So enjoy High Hay Wood, no need to pack!"

Owl turned to Mar, with a knowing wink.
She winked right back, or did she just blink?

Mar was grateful to our Lakeland clan,
And to Wainwright for his cunning plan.

"As for Bristle, Ping and young Peg too.
I couldn't feel more proud of you."

Ping, Peg and I, once again safe to play.
The threat from the Yankee Greys gone away.

Safe from danger we should have stayed,
Knowing the future would make us afraid.

Mar's fact file

Red Squirrels:

- Number about 140,000 in Britain, about 15,000 in England
- Numbers reduced by 95% in the last 50 years (the introduction of grey squirrels in 19th century is the main reason for the decline of the reds)
- Prefer coniferous forests as they eat cones, shoots, fungi and berries
- Make large dreys out of twigs, lined with moss, leaves and bark in branch forks
- Have litters of between 2 and 6 known as kittens
- Bury excess food or hide it in tree hollows
- Are most active in the mornings and late afternoons, resting in the middle of the day
- Do not hibernate but eat a lot in autumn to stock up for winter
- Are about 20cm long with tail length being 20cm
- Long tails help them to balance and steer and to keep them warm when sleeping
- Have strong hind legs and can swim
- Their greatest threats are predators, viruses and changes to landscape
- Can be seen in the Lake District at Dodd Wood, Keswick; Allan Bank, Grasmere; Whinlatter Park, Keswick; Haweswater Hotel, Bampton; Greystoke Forest, Penrith; Acorn Bank, Temple Sowerby; Rydal Hall; Lingholm; Keswick, Brockhole Visitors Centre

Grey Squirrels:

- Number about 2.5 million in Britain
- Were brought over from North America in the 1870's as ornamental species for the grounds of stately homes
- Spread a disease called 'squirrel pox virus', fatal to reds while greys are immune to it. Symptoms are skin ulcers, lesions, scabs and lethargy
- Are twice the weight of reds and eat more food. They raid reds' stores of hidden food
- Can eat acorns, unlike reds, so they survive better where there are oak trees

Lake Windermere at ten and a half miles long, is the largest natural lake in England.

High Hay Wood can be found on circular walk from Windermere to Orrest Head, extended through St Catherine's Wood. According to Wainwright, "Here the promised land is seen in all its glory."

Helm Crag sits at the end of a ridge above Grasmere. The summit, with its distinctive craggy rock formation gives it the title of The Lion and the Lamb or The Lion Couchant. Walkers can scramble up the 'lion' rocks to the summit.

Morecambe Bay Estuary lies between Lancashire and Cumbria. 120 square miles of sand can be seen when tide is out. It is the largest inter-tidal area of sand and mudflats in UK. It is designated as an 'area of outstanding beauty'. The Bay is notorious for its quicksand and fast moving tides (the tide can come in as fast as a horse can run). In 1821 a royal mail coach became stuck in the sand and a man drowned. In 1846 nine young people drowned, crossing the Bay at night. In 2004 twenty-three cockle pickers drowned when they were cut off by tides.

Beatrix Potter (1886-1943) is one of the best loved, best-selling children's authors. She wrote and illustrated a total of 28 books which have been translated into more than 35 languages and sold over 100 million copies. Following the success of her books she bought 15 farms. She married Ambleside solicitor, William Heelis, at age of 47. She was a great supporter of National Trust, founded in 1895, and a keen campaigner on conservation issues. She left all her farms and 4,000 acres of land to the National Trust.

Alfred Wainwright (1907 -1991) was born in Blackburn. He moved to Kendal in 1941 as Borough Treasurer. His seven guide books became the standard reference work for Lake District walkers with over 2 million copies being sold. He wrote 40 other books and guides.

For my dear children, Matthew, Alexander and Emma (SH)

For Meg and Heidi, Abbie, Matthew and Finn (WE)

Remembering Judith

Published in 2017
by **Squirrel Sagas Ltd**
www.squirrelsagas.com

© Copyright Ellwood & Holme 2017

Illustrations by Sophie Holme
www.blackandwhitedaydreams.com

ISBN: 978-0-9956663-0-6

Book interior and cover layout by Russell Holden
www.pixeltweakspublications.com

Pixel tweaks
PUBLICATIONS

Printed by Stramongate Press Ltd, Kendal
www.stramongatepress.co.uk

From 'Bristle the Red' by Wendy Ellwood Illustrated by Sophie Holme